MW00632833

STORY MONSTERS
AMONG US

A BRIEF HISTORY OF HUMAN STORYTELLING

CONRAD J. STORAD
ILLUSTRATED BY JEFF YESH

STORY MONSTERS®
PRESS
Chandler, Arizona, United States

Copyright ©2022 Story Monsters LLC

All rights reserved. No part of this book may be used or reproduced in any manner whatsoever or stored in any database or retrieval system without written permission except in the case of brief quotations used in critical articles and reviews. Requests for permissions should be addressed to:

Linda F. Radke, Publisher
Story Monsters Press
An imprint of Story Monsters LLC
4696 W. Tyson St.
Chandler, AZ 85226
(480) 940-8182
Publisher@storymonsters.com
www.StoryMonstersPress.com

Publisher's Cataloging-In-Publication Data

Names: Storad, Conrad J., author. | Yesh, Jeff, 1971- illustrator.
Title: Story monsters among us : a brief history of human storytelling /
    by Conrad J. Storad ; illustrated by Jeff Yesh.
Description: Chandler, Arizona, United States : Story Monsters Press,
    [2022] | Interest age level: 007-012. | Includes Words to Learn at
    end of book and a downloadable free curriculum guide will be available at
    www.StoryMonstersAmongUsBook.com. | Summary: "... guides readers of all
    ages through the evolution of storytelling, from the Chauvet Cave painters
    of southern France to the brothers Grimm"--Provided by publisher.
Identifiers: ISBN 9781589852426 (paperback) | ISBN 9781589852433
    (ebook Kindle)
Subjects: LCSH: Storytelling--History--Comic books, strips, etc. | CYAC:
    Storytelling--History--Cartoons and comics. | LCGFT: Graphic novels.
Classification: LCC LB1042 .S76 2022 (print) | LCC LB1042 (ebook) | DDC
    372.677--dc23

Printed in the United States of America

Illustrations and Design: Jeff Yesh
Editor: Paul M. Howey
Proofreaders: Ruthann Meyer, Cristy Bertini
Project Manager: Patti Crane

To Laurie,
My beautiful wife, my muse, my best friend.
And for all of my grandchildren...

Never stop reading. Never stop learning!
– CJS

Story Monsters are always
among us.

INTRODUCTION

The Power of Story ...
Past, Present, and Future

People love to tell stories. We love to listen to stories. We love to read stories. We love to watch stories. Stories have been a part of us from the very beginning. Why? The answer is simple. Humans are storytelling creatures.

We have rich cultures and many languages. Our large brains give us the ability to learn, understand, and remember. The brain can translate our thoughts and dreams into stories. Best of all, it allows us to share these stories with others in both spoken and written form.

Of course, some creatures have brains bigger than ours. They, too, can learn and communicate. But it is our ability to create and share stories that sets humans apart. Storytelling helps form the foundation for all human teaching and learning. We can't help ourselves. We love to tell stories. We always have, just not always in the same way as we do today.

Thousands of years ago, there were no books, no television, and no Internet. In fact, there was no written language of any kind. Spoken language was very primitive. But early humans still shared stories. How? They painted images on the walls of caves.

Human language got more sophisticated as time moved forward. Still, nothing was written down. That's because no one knew how to write. Stories were shared aloud in spoken form.

Every group of people, every tribe, every village, had a storyteller. The storyteller knew **ALL** the stories of the people. Every story was memorized.

In ancient times, people gathered around a campfire in the village center where they listened for hours to the storyteller. When the weather turned cold, the best place to listen to stories was near the fireplace after a tasty supper.

If you were a child growing up a long time ago, you had to listen. And if you were a very good listener, you learned the stories. You might even have grown up to become a storyteller yourself. In this way, for thousands of years, stories were passed along from one generation to the next.

Eventually, people learned how to write. The invention of written language led to books. The creation of books allowed for stories to be shared in new ways. We are lucky to be living today because we have books in many forms. We have libraries large and small. We also have the Internet and computers that allow for the preservation of all stories across time.

We are not alone

From the early days of painting on the walls of caves, humans have never been alone in their love for stories. Something else has always been watching and listening. These watchers are shy. These listeners do not want to be seen. They come in many sizes and forms. They are **Story Monsters**.

Do Story Monsters spring directly from the human imagination itself? Or do they come from somewhere else? No one is certain.

Story Monsters are **shapeshifters** that can assume the form of many things. They might be the size of a pea or as large as an oak tree.

In ancient days, Story Monsters often took the form of elves, dwarfs, trolls, or giants with a single eye. They might appear as flame-spewing dragons, three-headed dogs, or as a monstrous woman with hair made of venomous snakes. In other lands, they appeared as dancing goddesses with many arms or different animal heads. They could show themselves as leprechauns, hump-backed flute players, ugly witches, snarling wolves, or as beautiful princesses with long flowing hair. One might even appear as a little girl in a red cape walking through the woods on the way to grandma's house.

Story Monsters are still here in modern times. They still come in many sizes and shapes. Today they might look like big red dogs or curious little monkeys. Some can appear as a wooden puppet with a long nose or a cat with a tall striped hat. They've been seen as talking frogs or even an aardvark with round glasses. Others have reported seeing a Story Monster as a very flat little boy or as a long rattlesnake who teaches her babies. One can even appear as a little boy wizard with a jagged scar on his forehead.

One thing is certain: Story Monsters love stories. If someone is reading a book or telling a story, you can be sure that at least one Story Monster is somewhere near. They can be anywhere and everywhere. Story Monsters are always among us.

Keep your eyes and ears open, and never stop reading!

ANCIENT PAST

31,000 Years Ago

Deep inside Chauvet Cave

(Present day southern France)

Four glowing eyes watch from the shadowy recess of a cave. Each round eye blinks slowly, one after another as the little monster watches.

Shadows dance across a rough wall in the flickering light of a smoldering fire.

The floor is littered with bits and pieces of bone. In the corner is the skull of a bear.

A muscular human presses the palm of his hand against the wall. He leaves a red mark next to dozens of other handprints.

Above his mark is a freshly painted picture of a black deer. There are lots of other images in black and red. There are paintings of horses and bears and a musk ox. There are lions and rhinos and bison. In one corner is the picture of an owl. A panther is in another.

Are these pictures telling the story of a great hunt? Or are they something else?

The little monster watches and remembers.

ANCIENT PAST
14,800 years ago
Near the western edge of Winnemucca Lake
(Present day northwest Nevada)

The tiny monster pulls back deeper into the scrubby bushes. It wants to watch, but is careful not to be seen.

Its four eyes strain to see a pile of boulders near the edge of the lake. That is where the human is busy scratching a **PETROGLYPH** into the soft limestone.

Wiping her brow, the woman steps back to admire the work.

It's taken her hours to carve a complex series of swirls into the rock.

Near this new image are older carvings. There are lines and pits and shapes that look like diamonds. Others look like trees and flowers, even the veins of a leaf.

What do they mean? What stories do they tell? The little monster watches, and remembers.

ANCIENT PAST

More than 6,000 years ago

Within the walls of Ur in ancient Sumer near the Euphrates River

(Present day southern Iraq near the Persian Gulf)

The king's scribe carefully presses the stylus into a tablet of soft clay.

He forms line after line of wedge-shaped impressions called *PICTOGRAPHS*.

The symbols contain information from the king. When finished, the tablets will be sent to merchants in villages far from the king's great city.

Hidden in the corner behind a stack of reed baskets is a little four-eyed monster. It watches closely and makes no sound. There is no storyteller speaking. There are no words to be heard.

To understand the king's message, the creature must learn to read and understand the meaning of each new **CUNEIFORM "WORD-SIGN"** being pressed into the clay.

There is much work to be done.

mmm...???

ANCIENT PAST
More than 5,500 years ago
Inside a temple close to the great Egyptian city of Luxor on the Nile River

The little monster was hiding behind a stone column inside a beautiful temple. A group of priests dressed in white linen were working on a huge wall just a few feet away.

With careful, precise strokes, they painted colorful images of gods and goddesses.

On the wall were lines and lines of symbols called hieroglyphs.

As the little monster watched, its head and body changed shape to match those images.

First, it looked like a jackal with black skin and the tail of a lion.

Then, it became a one-eyed falcon with a muscular man's body.

It slowly melted into the shape of a powerful man with blue skin.

Suddenly, it looked like **ISIS**, a beautiful golden goddess.

There were lots more stories to read on the walls of the temple.

ANCIENT PAST

More than 4,000 years ago

At the bedside of a prince in the Mesopotamian city of Uruk

The young prince squirmed in his bed. Sleep would not come.

Please, Mama, tell me the story of the great **HERO-KING**.

Young one, I've told you the tale of **GILGAMESH** so many times. But all right, it is a wonderful story. It begins...

ANCIENT PAST

ABOUT 400 B.C.

In an olive grove just outside the city of Athens in Greece

The old teacher was just finishing a story for a group of young students. They all sat relaxed in the shade of several twisted olive trees.

So remember, the once **LAZY GRASSHOPPER** had learned from the ants.

He made a plan, worked hard, and stored food during the summer. Now, like the ants, he would not go hungry when winter's cold arrived.

AESOP was a great storyteller. He told this tale to my father's father more than 100 years ago.

A long-eared rabbit crouched nearby in a pile of rocks. For a brief second it seemed to change shape and shimmered in the sun.

I never get tired of **AESOP'S FABLES**.

ANCIENT PAST

ABOUT 300 B.C.
A palace in southern India

Three young princes sat cross-legged on the palace floor.
A small jade statue sat on a stone pedestal a few feet away.

It had many arms and
many eyes. The statue
appeared to move, just
a bit. But no one noticed.

The boys listened closely to the words of a white-haired sage as he recounted a story from the **PANCHATANTRA**. This one was about a king and a monkey.

Each fable he told included humans and animals of many kinds. The tales were entertaining. But each story had a larger purpose.

The teacher's stories touched on important themes. Some were about love and hatred. Others dealt with courage and cowardice, or generosity and cruelty. To become wise and able rulers, the princes must learn the messages within the stories.

ANCIENT PAST

About 1,900 years ago

A flower garden in China's Hunan Province during the Han Dynasty

The little monster had observed humans and listened to their stories for tens of thousands of years. It watched them create languages and learn to preserve those stories using pictures and symbols. Humans were smart. Some painted pictures on cave walls, leather, and wood. Others chiseled the symbols on rock or pressed them into clay.

In China, humans had perfected ways to use ink and dyes to record beautiful images on long sheets of cloth. Now, a fellow named **CAI LUN** was creating something brand new. The little monster watched from a bed of colorful flowers.

The man mixed water with mulberry bark, hemp and rags. Then he mashed it into pulp and pressed out the liquid to form thin mats. He hung the mats to dry in the sun.

Cai Lun called his creation ... **PAPER**.

This could change **EVERYTHING!**

HISTORIC PAST

Around the year 1100 A.D.

In the kiva of a Zuni pueblo

(Present day western New Mexico)

The **VILLAGE OF GREAT KIVAS** was a wonderful place to live. On special evenings, members of the tribe sat quietly near a crackling fire and listened to the shaman. He was a most respected elder.

HISTORIC PAST

Around the year 1275 A.D.

A scriptorium at the Franciscan Friary in York, Britain

The little monster enjoyed hanging around the scriptoriums of monasteries throughout Europe. For centuries, it had watched monks of many orders in Italy, France, Belgium, and Spain. They were all skilled at creating beautiful illuminated books on **VELLUM**.

But these monks in York were creating something spectacular. It was called a **BESTIARY**. They painted some of the images and words using real gold and silver.

The book would include the description of dozens and dozens of animals and creatures. Some were real and some were imaginary.

Each page was filled with colorful images. There were lions, griffins, birds, serpents, and sea creatures. There were eagles, elephants, unicorns, dragons, and a three-headed dog.

What great fun I will have!

I'll get plenty of **MORPHING** practice.

POOF!

BLAM!

HISTORIC PAST

Sometime during the summer in 1602
Globe Theatre in Stratford-upon-Avon, England

Back inside the theater, actors were preparing the stage for the next performance.

BOOM!

HISTORIC PAST

Around the year 1810
City of Hesse-Kassel in central Germany

The Grimm brothers—Jacob and Wilhelm—were hard at work reading and sorting. Respected scholars, their plan was to publish a collection of folk tales and poems, a total of 200 stories in all. They'd listened to storytellers and collected stories from across Europe for years. Manuscripts and books of all sizes were piled everywhere.

We must include the story of **HANSEL** and **GRETEL**.

The little monster had plenty of places to hide as it watched and listened. It was in love with the work of these German brothers.

RECENT PAST
Sometime in late 1961
Ted Geisel's home office in La Jolla, California

The little monster absolutely loved hanging around the bearded man's office to watch him work. It was so easy to blend in and not be noticed. Becoming a green Grinch was simple. Looking like a cat with a tall striped hat was a bit trickier.

This **DR. SEUSS** fellow is a writer who fits my style.

Last year's story about the **GREEN EGGS AND HAM** was kind of different. I liked his rhymes about the red and blue fish a lot better.

The monster climbed to the top of the desk to sneak a peek at the author's newest manuscript. Some illustrations were scribbled on paper as well.

PRESENT DAY
A March afternoon in 2019
An elementary school library in Phoenix, Arizona

The school library was a magical place. Mrs. Krebs, the librarian, made it that way. Of course, there were books of every kind. There were comics, mysteries, adventures, and scary stories. There were books about planets, flowers, reptiles, insects, and animals of every shape and size.

Everywhere you looked there was something fun to see. Stuffed animals, puppets, and statues of book characters sat on every shelf. Colorful murals filled with story themes covered every wall. There was a giant red dog, blue things, a boy wizard, dragons, a curious monkey, and a princess with long red hair. The furry four-eyed monster sat on a shelf in plain view.

NEAR FUTURE

Late in the 21st century
The relaxation center at Mars Base Alpha

The hydroponic garden's misters shut off with a loud click.

CLICK!

Droplets of water glistened on the leaves of vines loaded with ripe tomatoes.

Matted with red dust, the little monster looked like a tomato that had sprouted four bulging eye stalks. It peered through a foggy window into the relaxation center next door.

A dozen human scientists and engineers lived at Mars Base Alpha.

MARS BASE ALPHA

MB22

Twice as many robots worked there around the clock.

For the humans, off-duty time meant fun time...or story time. They could access any of **TENS OF THOUSANDS** of books and videos from the computer library. Personal tablets displayed text. The 25-foot vid-wall could blaze to life with 3D movies, complete with "sense-surround."

The little monster loved living on Mars.

FUTURE

100 years from now...or less

On a starship speeding toward a distant solar system

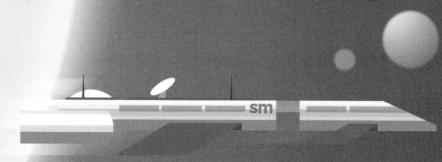

The 100 human colonists aboard the starship were safe inside their hibernation pods. They would wake from **CRYOSLEEP** in a few months. That's when the ship was scheduled to enter orbit around the new planet.

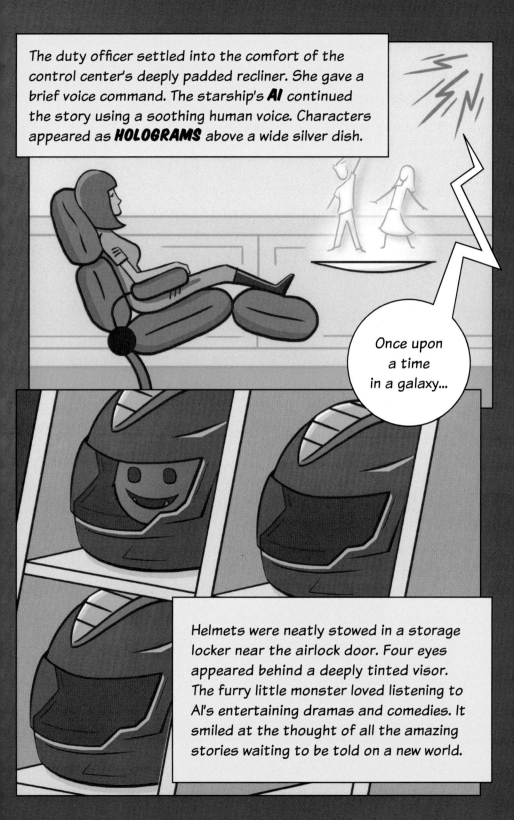

The duty officer settled into the comfort of the control center's deeply padded recliner. She gave a brief voice command. The starship's **AI** continued the story using a soothing human voice. Characters appeared as **HOLOGRAMS** above a wide silver dish.

Once upon a time in a galaxy...

Helmets were neatly stowed in a storage locker near the airlock door. Four eyes appeared behind a deeply tinted visor. The furry little monster loved listening to AI's entertaining dramas and comedies. It smiled at the thought of all the amazing stories waiting to be told on a new world.

INTO THE FUTURE...

Storytelling has always been a process unique to humans across our entire history. We have sophisticated cultures and rich languages. It's in our DNA, the love of story. It is what sets apart from other creatures on the planet.

We can't help ourselves. We are storytelling creatures. Storytelling allows us to impose the order of story structure onto the chaos of daily life. We can't live in silence. We all need to lead "storied" lives.

What are you waiting for? Get out there and start observing, listening, and participating via story. It's time to start your own new chapters.

Conrad J. Storad
Barberton, Ohio – October 2020

WORDS TO LEARN

AI: The abbreviation for Artificial Intelligence. In the future, an AI might be used to monitor and run all the systems on a spaceship and allow humavns the time to do other tasks.

bestiary: A special book created by European monks during medieval times. The book contained colorful illustrations and stories about real and imaginary animals. Each story had a moral message.

cryosleep: From science fiction stories, the process in which a space traveler is put into a state of hibernation or suspended animation inside a very cold chamber or pod. Scientists are working to make the process a reality.

cuneiform: Words or symbols written in clay as wedge-shaped characters.

hieroglyphic: A system of writing based on the use of pictorial characters. The ancient Egyptians told stories by painting hieroglyphs on temple walls and in the tombs of pharaohs and other rulers.

hologram: A three-dimensional image produced using intersecting beams of laser light. Computers help to control the image.

Katsina: An ancestral spirit important to the Pueblo peoples of the American Southwest. The Hopis, Zunis, and other Native Americans have names for more than 500 Katsina. They act as intermediaries between humans and the gods.

kiva: A round structure, partly underground, used for special ceremonies by the Hopis, Zunis, and other Pueblo peoples of the American Southwest.

morph: To transform from the image of one object into that of another.

Panchatantra: From ancient India, a collection of animal-based fables written in prose and verse. Each has a moral lesson to teach.

petroglyph: An image of shapes, people, or animals carved or scratched onto the surface of rocks. Petroglyphs are thought to be an early form of storytelling.

pictograph: Paintings of animals, shapes, or people usually found on stones, the walls of caves, or in places protected from the weather.

scriptorium: In Latin, the word means "a place for writing." They were usually rooms in medieval European monasteries where scribes worked to write, copy, or illuminate manuscripts.

shaman: Among many tribal peoples, a person who acted as a connection between the natural and supernatural worlds. Sometimes called a medicine man, a shaman used magic to cure illness or invoke the help of spiritual forces to protect the tribe.

shapeshifter: A person or creature with the ability to change their physical form at will.

vellum: Sometimes called parchment, a specially prepared animal skin used as a material to write on. Vellum is made from calf skin and is a very high quality material.

ACTIVITY GUIDE

written by Jean Kilker, M.A., M.Ed., NBPTS

As you've learned from reading this story, all cultures since the beginning of humans have been storytellers. Now it's your turn! With your parent or other adult, use these hands-on activities to help you become a dynamic storyteller.

PREHISTORIC PAST – Cave Art and Petroglyphs

Take a virtual tour of the French caves:

» Chauvet cave paintings: youtu.be/3OLaNtKoJFk
» Lascaux cave and rock art around the world: bradshawfoundation.com/lascaux/

Discuss.

1. How realistic are these drawings?
2. What do you think made the different colors?
3. What are the animals?
4. Do we have these animals today?

Be creative.

Make your own cave paintings with finger paint:

» You'll need: butcher paper (a paper grocery bag cut open works well to mimic stone walls) and fingerpaint.
» Options for finger paint:
  · Chocolate and vanilla pudding.
  · Tub of vanilla frosting and food coloring. Split frosting into four or more small bowls. With an adult's help, add a few of drops of food coloring: red, green, black and yellow to each bowl.
» Choose three animals and your handprint to draw.

Interested in more storytelling activities?

Download the full activity guide at: StoryMonstersAmongUsBook.com

---

THE CREATIVE TEAM

Conrad Storad – Author

Conrad J. Storad is the national award-winning author and editor of more than 50 science and nature books for young readers. Many of Storad's books reflect his interest and fascination with Nature's amazing creatures. An accomplished storyteller, Storad has "edu-tained" more than 1 million students and teachers across the country with his programs and writing workshops that promote reading and science literacy.

After 33 years living and working in Tempe, Arizona, Storad and his wife Laurie returned to their hometown of Barberton, Ohio, where he was a 2017 inductee to the city's Walk of Fame.

Jeff Yesh – Illustrator

Jeff Yesh is a freelance illustrator and graphic designer whose award-winning work has been featured in multiple children's books, including *A Squirrel's Story—A True Tale*. Yesh is also the artistic talent behind the Story Monsters character and is the graphic designer for the award-winning Story Monsters Ink, the literary resource for parents, teachers, and librarians. Yesh graduated from Indiana State University with a Bachelor of Fine Arts in Graphic Design. He lives in Indiana with his wife, two daughters, and a slew of pets.

STORY MONSTERS®
PRESS

Story Monsters Press – Publisher

Story Monsters Press, an imprint of Story Monsters LLC, is a publisher of children's books that offer hope, value differences, and build character. Each book also includes a curriculum guide complementing the story for parents and educators to use with young readers.